The Other Side of the Story

by Isabel Gallego
illustrated by Christian Slade

Chapters

Harcourt

Orlando   Boston   Dallas   Chicago   San Diego

Visit *The Learning Site!*

www.harcourtschool.com

It's Not Fair!

It is Monday at Shawnee Heights Middle School. The staff of the school newspaper is finding it hard to concentrate. Everyone is talking about a story in Sunday's *Times-Clarion*. The story is about problems at nearby Shawnee Heights Mall.

"These store owners blame the noise and damage on 'young people' at the mall," Kim says. "My friends and I like to hang out there after school. We're not responsible for any violations of the law. Yet when they say 'young people,' they're talking about us, too."

"Right! It's not fair!" says Alfred. "They want
an ordinance keeping out people who aren't
customers. Well, I'm a customer, sometimes. I buy
clothes there. I go to the movies and I eat at the
food court. Are they going to kick me out when
I'm there just to meet friends?"

Wendy turns to Mr. Klein, the teacher who
helps them plan and write the school newspaper.
"Mr. Klein, you told us a reporter should get both
sides of a story," she says. "This reporter got only
the store owners' side. She didn't talk to any of
the 'young people' they're blaming for all the
trouble."

"Well," says Mr. Klein, "if you feel that way,
why don't you write an op-ed piece for the *Times-
Clarion*?"

"A what?" several students ask.

"An op-ed piece. It's short for 'opinion-editorial,' or 'opposite of the editorial.'"

Mr. Klein opens the daily newspaper. "See, here's the editorial page of the *Times-Clarion*. You all know what an editorial is."

Dwayne nods. "Sure, it's opinions of the paper's editorial staff about current events and things."

"Right. Now, across from it is the op-ed page. This is where the paper prints other people's opinions. Most of them are by well-known writers or public figures. Here's an article by Senator Mansfield. It explains where she stands on the issue of funding for schools."

"But most papers also have a free-speech column. The *Times-Clarion* calls it Open Forum. Anyone can write on any subject." Mr. Klein points at one of the letters. "This man wants the city council to postpone its vote on the new bike path. He thinks the ordinance is unfair to property owners along the path."

"Why would the *Times-Clarion* print anything we wrote?" asks Amanda.

"Why wouldn't they—if it's effective and well written?" Mr. Klein answers.

"Here's our chance to tell those store owners what we think of them," Alfred says.

"Sure, if it makes you feel better," Mr. Klein says. "But if you want it to be *read*, write about the issue, not people. The paper won't print an 'attack piece.' You can't write something that's false and meant to damage someone's reputation."

"That's strange," says Kim. "This article about the young people at the mall is mostly false. It damages our reputation, but the newspaper printed it anyway!"

"I'd call that an attack piece!" says Alfred.

All the students nod in agreement.

Mr. Klein finally nods, too. "I see what you mean. It's not fair. Still, you can use the Open Forum to help people understand the other side of the story."

"Let's do it!" says Wendy.

Getting to Work

The students work on their op-ed piece that day and the next. They all contribute ideas. Then Dwayne writes the first draft.

Amanda reads it and says, "This is too long. I checked out the Open Forum columns for the past week. They're all 500 words or less."

"But these are all important ideas," Dwayne says. "What can we cut?"

"You can find something to take out," says Mr. Klein. "A shorter piece can often be more effective. Besides, you want to get it in the newspaper soon, or the mall story will be old news."

"I don't think we should repeat so much of what Mr. Bell said," Dwayne suggests. He points at a paragraph in their letter. It tells how Mr. Bell caught teenagers shoplifting in his store. "If we repeat the part about the shoplifting, people will think he's right about keeping all of us out."

"I agree," says Kim. "That's one part we can take out. Now, what else can we cut?"

The students go back to work and finish their article on Wednesday. They all read it very carefully to make sure it makes sense. They use the spell-checker, too.

Then Wendy reads it one more time. She finds a place where they left out a word. They type in the word and print the letter again. Then they mail it to the *Times-Clarion*.

The paper's editors receive dozens of letters for the Open Forum every week. They can print only six of them. What's more, they cannot spend a lot of time making their choices. However, this well-written piece by middle-school students catches their attention.

The students' letter appears in Monday's issue. Everyone at school is talking about it. Here's what it says.

Which Young People?

Recently a story appeared in the *Times-Clarion* about problems at the Shawnee Heights Mall. Store owners were angry about stealing and property damage. They were also concerned that "rowdy behavior by young people, especially around the food court," was driving away customers.

The story quoted Mr. Lamar Bell of Bell's Camera Shop. He suggested that the people responsible for the "rowdy behavior"—mostly loud talk—are also stealing and destroying property. He wants the city council to pass a law preventing young people from gathering at the mall.

"The council must place this item on its agenda," Bell said in the article. "Our stores just cannot stay open if this behavior continues. We pay taxes in this community, and we want something done."

Well, Mr. Bell, we are the "young people" of this community. We'd like something done, too.

First of all, we'd like an apology from you and the other store owners. We know that some young people get noisy. We understand why you don't want your property damaged or stolen. But it is unfair to hold a certain group of people responsible only because of their age.

Most of us who come to the mall do not cause problems. We meet our friends, shop, and buy snacks. Why do you lump all of us in with those few who cause trouble?

We'd also like an apology from the *Times-Clarion*. A news story is supposed to report both sides of an issue. Your reporter presented only the store owners' side. Why didn't she talk to any of the "young people" at the food court? Why didn't she postpone judgment until we had a chance to explain our side?

She might have asked us why we come to the mall. This is what we would have told her: because it's somewhere to go. Shawnee Heights has very few places for young people to go and have fun.

We, too, would like the city council to put an item on its agenda. We'd like them to consider funding a community center in Shawnee Heights.

We could use a gym and a game room. A swimming pool would be nice, too. But mostly, we just need a place where we can relax and talk.

Like the store owners, our parents pay taxes in this community. We have a right to ask for something back. Maybe the store owners could put up part of the money for the center. Then the city could provide the rest.

That's an effective way to take care of what some people see as a problem at the mall. And we would have somewhere else to go.

Two days later Alfred hurries into the school newsroom with the morning newspaper. "Look at this!" he says. "Here's an article about the next city council meeting!"

"Why are you so excited?" Mr. Klein asks.

"The article has the agenda for the meeting. They're going to talk about a new community center!" Alfred tells them.

Everyone rushes over to check the agenda. They all talk at once.

"That's great!" says Wendy. "People must have read our letter! We're going to have somewhere to go! All we had to do was tell the other side of the story!"